Contents

Unstressed vowels 1

Remember

In longer words, some syllables and vowels are difficult to hear when words are spoken normally.

Say the syllables clearly and stress hidden vowels and syllables.

chocolate – say: choc-o-late   interesting – say: in-ter-est-ing

Try it

1 Write these words split into syllables to make the unstressed vowel clear.

a) definite _____   e) separate _____   i) relevant _____

b) messenger _____   f) considering _____   j) several _____

c) envelope _____   g) average _____   k) privilege _____

d) general _____   h) desperate _____   l) literate _____

2 Write in the missing vowel or vowels to spell these words.

a) sim __ l __ r   f) instr __ m __ nt   k) ben __ fit   p) h __ riz __ n

b) reg __ l __ r   g) secr __ t __ ry   l) c __ mp __ ny   q) gar __ ge

c) reas __ n   h) veg __ t __ ble   m) pop __ l __ r   r) man __ ge

d) dand __ li __ n   i) purp __ se   n) wiz __ rd   s) hurr __ cane

e) mir __ cle   j) chall __ nge   o) vill __ __ n   t d __ vel __ p

Read–cover–write

Read this sentence and remember it. Then cover it and write it underneath.

The company was desperate to hit its regular target.

_____

Check your spellings with the answers on page 40. Test yourself, or get a friend to test you.

I can spell all the words on this page. ☐

I can say the syllables to spell longer words with unstressed vowels. ☐

Schofield&Sims

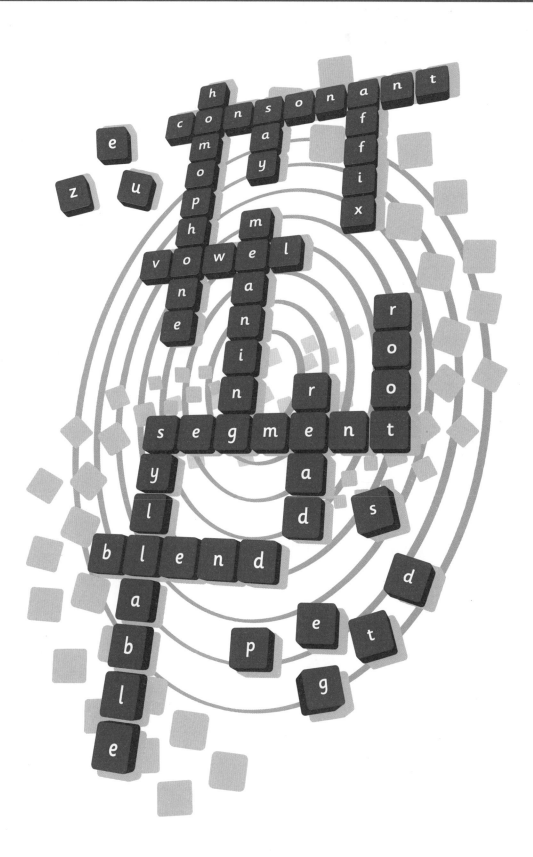

Spelling 5

Name

Introduction

Learning to spell is important because correct spelling helps others to read your writing. Being able to spell also helps you as a writer. If you can spell easily, you have more time to think about the content of your writing.

This book helps you learn to spell. It shows you patterns, rules and strategies that will help you spell sets of words. It also teaches you how to spell some 'tricky' words that don't follow the normal patterns.

Finding your way around

There are six sections in this book. Each section has five pages and then a 'tricky words' or 'topic words' page. Revision pages towards the end of some sections check that you have remembered earlier spellings. Each of the main pages is made up of three parts.

Remember	**Try it**	**Read–cover–write**	
This tells you the spelling pattern or rule that you will practise. There are examples to help you.	Here you use the pattern to help you spell words. Write the words in the spaces.	Here you practise spelling words in a sentence – just as you do when you are writing.	Top tips appear on some pages. They provide extra help, so make sure you read them.

The correct answers to the questions are given at the back of this book on pages 40 to 47. Each page you work through tells you the number of the page where you can find the answers. This number is given in the coloured box near the foot of the page.

How to begin

Write your name on the cover. Then work carefully through the first page of activities. When you finish a page, turn to the answers page. **Use the answers page to check that your spellings are correct.** Practise each word that you got wrong. Write the word correctly. Then look at where you went wrong. Write the word again correctly. Write it five times. When you think you can spell all the words, get a friend to test you. Again, practise any words you get wrong. You will find a box like this at the bottom of the page.

I can spell all the words on this page. ☐   I can choose the correct spelling of homophones. ☐

Tick these boxes when you are confident about spelling all the words and using the pattern or rule when you are writing.

Now make sure that you spell all the words correctly in everything that you write.

Unstressed vowels 2

Remember

Some vowel sounds get lost when affixes are added.   fattening   describe

Think of the root word, prefixes and suffixes to help spell words like this.

Try it

1 Underline the unstressed vowels. Write each word so you can see the root word and affix.

a) offering _____

b) freedom _____

c) original _____

d) marvellous _____

e) prepare _____

f) considerable _____

g) miserable _____

h) formal _____

i) prosperous _____

j) poisonous _____

k) natural _____

l) tomorrow _____

2 Read the clues and complete the words.

a) a deaf_____ noise (very loud)

b) road wide_____ (making bigger)

c) jewel_____ box (for trinkets)

d) pencil sharp_____
(makes pencils sharp)

e) a fright_____ experience (scary)

f) hair straight_____ (styling device)

g) an imagine_____ world (make believe)

h) teeth white_____ (makes teeth white)

Read–cover–write

Read this sentence and remember it. Then cover it and write it underneath.

The miserable creature let out a deafening scream.

_____

Check your spellings with the answers on page 40. Test yourself, or get a friend to test you.

I can spell all the words on this page. ☐

I can use root words and affixes to identify unstressed vowels. ☐

Words ending 'er'

Remember

An unstressed 'er' sound at the end of a word might be spelt **er**, **ar**, **or** or **re**.   protester   sugar   instructor   genre

Stressing the ending will help you remember the correct spelling.

Try it

1 Complete these lists of people. Write in the missing ending.
   Use **er**, **or** or **ar**.

   a) A robb____, an arch____ and a pott____ visited the prison____.

   b) The sail____, the doct____ and the invent____ met the inspect____.

   c) A begg____ and a burgl____ met the vic____ in the cellar.

   d) An auth____, an edit____, an act____ and a direct____ met an art collect____.

   e) The groc____, the bak____, the build____ and the butch____ need a custom____.

2 Complete these words. Add **or**, **ar** or **re**.

   a) sens____   f) operat____   k) horr____   p) elevat____   u) caterpill____

   b) coll____   g) gramm____   l) profess____   q) err____   v) terr____

   c) mirr____   h) monit____   m) calend____   r) sol____   w) spons____

   d) met____   i) fib____   n) lit____   s) theat____   x) cent____

   e) visit____   j) radiat____   o) reflect____   t) alligat____   y) tract____

Read–cover–write

Read this sentence and remember it. Then cover it and write it underneath.

The professor hung a calendar in the corridor at the research centre.

_____

Check your spellings with the answers on page 40. Test yourself, or get a friend to test you.

I can spell all the words on this page. ☐   I can spell words with **er**, **ar**, **or** and **re** endings. ☐

6

Words ending ary, ory and ery

Remember

Stress the vowel to help distinguish between ary, ory and ery endings.

Say: Jan-u-a-ry   fac-tor-y   scen-er-y

Try it

1 Complete these words by writing in ary, ory or ery.

a) myst_____   f) diction_____   k) Febru_____   p) batt_____

b) fact_____   g) deliv_____   l) recov_____   q) prim_____

c) mem_____   h) di_____   m) discov_____   r) second_____

d) nurs_____   i) forg_____   n) vict_____   s) ordin_____

e) burgl_____   j) arch_____   o) gloss_____   t) mis_____

2 Read the clues and complete the words.

a) bo_____ary (border)   f) su_____ary (summing up)

b) vo_____ary (unpaid)   g) ca_____ory (group or classification)

c) di_____ory (list of phone numbers)   h) mi_____ary (armed forces)

d) lo_____ery (prize draw)   i) ga_____ery (it displays art)

e) su_____ery (where doctors work)   j) ma_____ery (mechanical equipment)

Read–cover–write

Read this sentence and remember it. Then cover it and write it underneath.

Life was quite ordinary until I won the lottery last February.

_____

Check your spellings with the answers on page 40. Test yourself, or get a friend to test you.

I can spell all the words on this page. ☐   I can use ary, ory and ery in many words. ☐

Words ending 'shun'

Remember

There are different spellings for the 'shun' ending.
Use **tion** if it ends **t/te** and most other letters.   perfect → perfection
Use **cian** if the root word ends **ic**.   politic → politician
Use **sion** if the word ends **d/de** or **se**.   persuade → persuasion
Use **ssion** if the root word ends **ss** or **it**.   admit → admission

1 Add the correct 'shun' ending to the root word and write the noun.

a) direct _____   e) permit _____   i) complete _____

b) magic _____   f) optic _____   j) transfuse _____

c) intrude _____   g) reduce _____   k) impress _____

d) process _____   h) electric _____   l) include _____

2 Add **ate** to complete these verbs. Then use **tion** to write the noun.

a) oper _____, _____   f) imit _____, _____

b) celebr _____, _____   g) exagger _____, _____

c) communic _____, _____   h) ventil _____, _____

d) termin _____, _____   i) illustr _____, _____

e) demonstr _____, _____   j) equ _____, _____

Read–cover–write

Read this sentence and remember it. Then cover it and write it underneath.

The professional magician gave a demonstration of his illusion.

_____

Check your spellings with the answers on page 41. Test yourself, or get a friend to test you.

I can spell all the words on this page. ☐   I can spell words with 'shun' endings. ☐

Tricky words

Learn to spell these words. Take the word apart to look for the tricky bit.
Then build it up to learn to spell it.

Read and look.	Write it. Take the word apart.	Write it. Find the tricky bit.	Remember it. Cover it. Write it.	Check. ✓
eighth				
ninth				
twelfth				
truly				
skilful				
omit				
jury				
queue				
speech				
forest				

Read–cover–write

**Read each sentence and remember it. Then cover the table and the
sentence and write the sentence underneath.**

The jury listened carefully to the judge's speech.

_____

The golfer played a truly skilful shot to the ninth hole.

_____

Omit the twelfth question if you are unsure.

_____

Letter string **au**

Remember

The letter string **au** represents a different sound in different words.

caution   fault   Austria

Try it

1 Complete these words using **au**. Then copy each word into the correct box.

a) ____nt   d) be____ty   g) tr____ma   j) l____ghter

b) d____ghter   e) t____nt   h) dr____ght   k) n____ghty

c) s____sage   f) h____l   i) p____se   l) dinos____r

au makes an 'or' sound	au makes a different sound

2 All these words contain the **au** letter string. Read the clue and complete the word.

a) s_____ (a pot to cook in)

b) r_____rant (eat a meal there)

c) exh_____ (tired out)

d) h_____ty (proud, conceited)

e) ap_____ (a round of clapping)

f) l_____y (wash clothes there)

g) b_____ful (attractive)

h) a h_____ed house (with a ghost)

i) sl_____er (kill, slay)

j) cl_____ (part of a sentence)

Read–cover–write

Read this sentence and remember it. Then cover it and write it underneath.

A fault in the exhaust delayed the launch until August.

_____

Check your spellings with the answers on page 41. Test yourself, or get a friend to test you.

I can spell all the words on this page. ☐   I can spell words with the **au** letter string. ☐

Letter string **our**

Remember

The **our** letter string represents different sounds in different words.
flour   fourteen   journey

 Look for the word **our** in or at the end of words to help you spell them.

Try it

1 Add **our** to complete these pairs of words where it has the same sound.

a) _____selves – sc_____   f) glam_____ – hon_____

b) c_____age – n_____ish   g) fav_____ – vig_____

c) t_____ – det_____   h) m_____n – s_____ce

d) c_____t – c_____se   i) sav_____ – behavi_____

e) h_____ – dev_____   j) sav_____y – fav_____ite

2 All these words contain the **our** letter string. Read the clue and complete the word.

a) d_____p_____ (heavy rain)   g) la_____ (hard work)

b) od_____ (a smell, scent)   h) n_____ (lives next door)

c) v__p_____ (steam)   i) r__m_____ (gossip)

d) h____b_____ (place for ships)   j) t_____ist (someone on holiday)

e) m_____ful (sad)   k) h__m_____ (sense of _____)

f) arm_____ (protective clothing)   l) j_____ist (news reporter)

Read–cover–write

Read this sentence and remember it. Then cover it and write it underneath.

I recorded in my favourite journal the flavours, odours and colours.

_____

Letter string **ough**

Remember

The **ough** letter string can represent many different sounds.

Top tip Look for this letter string rather than relying on the sound.

Try it

1 Add **ough** to complete these words.

a) c_____   d) tr_____   g) bor_____   j) f_____t

b) t_____   e) r_____   h) d_____   k) pl_____

c) br_____t   f) b_____   i) th_____   l) thor_____

2 Find pairs of words in question 1 where **ough** has the same sound. Write the pairs below.

_____ and _____   _____ and _____

_____ and _____   _____ and _____

_____ and _____   _____ and _____

3 Read the clue and write the word. They all contain the **ough** letter string.

a) _____ (sufficient)   e) _____ (lack of rain)

b) _____ (past tense of seek)   f) _____ (even if)

c) _____ (should)   g) _____ (past tense of buy)

d) _____ (not thinking)   h) _____ (completely, entirely)

Read—cover—write

Read this sentence and remember it. Then cover it and write it underneath.

I thought throughout I had brought enough flour with me to make the dough.

_____

Check your spellings with the answers on page 41. Test yourself, or get a friend to test you.

I can spell all the words on this page. ☐   I can spell words with the **ough** letter string. ☐

Words with **ie** and **ei**

Remember

A long 'e' sound is often spelt **ie**, unless it comes after the letter **c**.

brief   deceit   Think: **i** before **e** except after **c** for long 'e'.

Try it

1 Use the rule to decide the correct spelling of these words. Write in **ie** or **ei**.

a) gr____f   d) misch____f   g) w____ld   j) n____ce   m) c____ling

b) rel____f   e) f____nd   h) rec____ve   k) ach____ve   n) conc____t

c) rec____pt   f) dec____ve   i) shr____k   l) gr____ve   o) perc____ve

 Letter strings **ie** and **ei** can also make other sounds.   s**ie**ve   w**ei**ght

2 Look for **ie** and **ei** in these words. Write over **ie** and **ei** in colour.
Then write the words in the correct box.

quiet   height   sleigh   view   reign   seize
fiery   weird   neither   veil   either   vein

ie not long 'e' sound	ei long 'a' sound	ei other sound

Read–cover–write

Read this sentence and remember it. Then cover it and write it underneath.

I believe the blow he received was so fierce it pierced his shield.

_____

Check your spellings with the answers on page 42. Test yourself, or get a friend to test you.

I can spell all the words on this page. ☐   I can spell words with **ie** and **ei** spelling patterns. ☐

13

Revision 1

1 Read this extract from a story. Check the spelling of words with common letter strings. Underline the words that are wrong. Write the correct spelling above them.

The knight came to a buetiful field of colorful flowers. The sight cheered

him and he laghed as he thought of the five peices of silver he beleived

he would recieve for rescuing the king's favorite dauhgter. But suddenly,

a mornful sound peirced the silence. His horse was thorughly spooked

and the knight's curage once more deserted him.

2 Write in the missing word.

a) Let's play Happy F_____.

b) Cars are built in f_____.

c) Paintings are displayed in art g_____.

d) A torch needs b_____.

e) Doctors work at s_____.

f) It brings back happy m_____.

g) es_____ (make a guess)

h) op_____ (work a machine)

i) na_____ (tell a story)

j) d_____ (show how it's done)

k) cr_____ (make, produce)

l) pu_____ (add commas)

3 Read this recount. Check the spelling of words for missing or incorrect vowels. Underline each word that is wrong. Write the correct spelling above it.

Yesturday I went cycling with my famaly. Mum said it would be intresting to try

something diffrent for a change. We must have cycled for sevral hours. None of

us fell off, which was quite good considring how differcult the path was. But then

the sky darkend and it was no suprise when it began to rain. Natrally we had

a misrable ride back. Still, I would defenately go again.

Check your spellings with the answers on page 42.

Topic words 1

Learn to spell these words. Take the word apart to look for the tricky bit. Then build it up to learn to spell it.

Read and look.	Write it. Take the word apart.	Write it. Find the tricky bit.	Remember it. Cover it. Write it.	Check. ✓
amenity				
facility				
region				
leisure				
inhabitant				
volcano				
Europe				
reservoir				
estuary				
erosion				

Read–cover–write

Read each sentence and remember it. Then cover the table and the sentence and write the sentence underneath.

Describe the amenities available to the community at the reservoir.

_____

_____

How many live volcanoes are there in Europe?

_____

Beware of coastal erosion close to the estuary.

_____

Words with soft c

Remember

A 's' sound is spelt **c** when it is followed by **i**, **e** or **y**.

decide   excellent   bicycle

Try it

1 Add **ce**, **ci** or **cy** to spell these words with a soft **c**.

a) de____mal   f) ____clone   k) in____dent   p) fas____nate

b) vacan____   g) de____nt   l) inno____nt   q) ____gar

c) re____te   h) coun____l   m) pro____ss   r) mer____

d) ____metery   i) suc____ss   n) s____nic   s) convin____

e) sin____re   j) ex____ed   o) fan____   t) capa____ty

2 All these words have a 's' sound spelt **c**. Read the clue and write the word.

a) c_____al (in the middle)   g) c_____er (tube shape)

b) c_____en (resident of a place) h) c_____a (watch films there)

c) c_____ry (100 years)   i) m_____nt (splendid, grand)

d) c_____st (rides a bike)   j) con_____ (a worry)

e) re_____t (latest, not long ago) k) s_____d (not fail)

f) d_____on (a choice)   l) c_____te (a paper award)

Read–cover–write

Read this sentence and remember it. Then cover it and write it underneath.

I recently saw a fascinating film at the cinema.

_____

Check your spellings with the answers on page 42. Test yourself, or get a friend to test you.

I can spell all the words on this page. ☐   I can spell words with soft **c** in them. ☐

16

Spelling patterns **ci**, **cu** and **cc**

Remember

The letter **c** sometimes combines with other letters to make different sounds.
ci = 'sh': appreciate official   **cu** = 'q': rescue   **cc** = 'x': access

Try it

1 Add the ending that makes the 'sh' sound in each word. Use **ian**, **ious**, **ial** or **ient**.

a) music_____

b) spac_____

c) optic_____

d) suspic_____

e) politic_____

f) delic_____

g) vic_____

h) anc_____

i) grac_____

j) lusc_____

k) financ_____

l) prec_____

m) consc_____

n) effic_____

o) spec_____

p) soc_____

q) suffic_____

r) artific_____

s) rac_____

t) malic_____

2 These words all have other special **c** spelling patterns. Read the clue and write the word.

a) ac_____te (speed up)

b) a_____t (mishap)

c) d_____nt (important file, papers)

d) sp_____ar (stunning)

e) ev_____te (leave in an emergency)

f) c_____s (nosy, ask a lot of questions)

g) ac_____t (way of speaking)

h) ec_____ic (odd, peculiar)

i) c_____te (work out in maths)

j) oc_____ (take up a space)

k) a_____ (exact)

l) p_____ar (strange, odd)

Read–cover–write

Read this sentence and remember it. Then cover it and write it underneath.

We appreciated the delicious meal and spectacular view.

_____

Check your spellings with the answers on page 42. Test yourself, or get a friend to test you.

I can spell all the words on this page. ☐   I can spell words where **c** makes different sounds. ☐

Words with soft g

Remember

A 'j' sound is often spelt **g** before the letters **e**, **i** and **y**.

digest   strange   giant   imagine   gym

Try it

1 These words all start with a soft **g**. Read the clue and write the word.

a) g_____ (huge)

b) g_____ (a mastermind)

c) g_____ (real, not fake)

d) g_____ (softly, lightly)

e) g_____ (acrobat)

f) g_____ (not mean)

g) g_____ (magical person in a bottle)

h) g_____ (bugs, bacteria)

i) g_____ (make a signal)

j) g_____ (turn, spin)

2 These words should all have a 'j' sound spelt **g** in the middle. Write the word correctly.

a) rijid _____

b) emerjency _____

c) dunjeon _____

d) gadjet _____

e) ajile _____

f) apolojy _____

g) orijin _____

h) lejend _____

i) enjineer _____

j) dijit _____

k) judjement _____

l) privileje _____

m) trajic _____

n) sujestion _____

o) ajent _____

p) exajerate _____

q) lojic _____

r) gorjeous _____

Read–cover–write

Read this sentence and remember it. Then cover it and write it underneath.

In general, a genuine agile gymnast will land gently.

_____

Check your spellings with the answers on page 43. Test yourself, or get a friend to test you.

I can spell all the words on this page. ☐   I can spell words with a soft 'g' sound. ☐

Silent letters

Remember

Some letters can have silent consonants attached to them.

w̲rong si̲g̲n succum̲b this̲tle rh̲yme k̲night autum̲n

 Top tip Say the silent letter or use a memory trick, for example: island – **is** land.

Try it

1 All these words have a silent consonant. Read the clue and write the word.

a) l_____ (an arm or leg)

b) _____st (truthful)

c) t_____ (burial place)

d) pl_____ (one who fixes leaks)

e) h_____c_____ (made by bees)

f) _____d (squeeze and press dough)

g) s_____ (odour, perfume)

h) s_____ (a plan)

i) re_____ (proof of payment)

j) hu_____ (push and jostle)

2 Complete these words using the pairs of letters in the pink box.

rh gn wr mn bt

a) dou____

b) ____ythm

c) ____etched

d) campai____

e) desi____

f) ____eath

g) rei____

h) ____ombus

i) ____ing

j) forei____

k) conde____

l) ____ino

m) colu____

n) su____le

o) resi____

p) ____ubarb

q) de____

r) ____ench

s) hy____

t) sole____

Read–cover–write

Read this sentence and remember it. Then cover it and write it underneath.

The plumber wrung his hands in doubt before picking up the wrench.

_____

Check your spellings with the answers on page 43. Test yourself, or get a friend to test you.

I can spell all the words on this page. ☐   I can spell words with silent letters. ☐

Words ending **ti** and **tu**

Remember

Endings beginning **ti** and **tu** create 'sh' and 'ch' sounds.
ti = 'sh': fiction   initial   fictitious   **tu** = 'ch': picture   actual

Try it

1 Add the ending that creates the 'sh' sound in these words. Use **ial, ious** or **ient**.

a) part_____   d) potent_____   g) ambit_____   j) caut_____

b) confident_____   e) scrumpt_____   h) pat_____   k) resident_____

c) infect_____   f) torrent_____   i) nutrit_____   l) essent_____

2 The missing words all have endings that begin with **ti** ('sh') or **tu** ('ch'). Read the clue and complete the word.

a) sub_____ savings (considerable, large)   h) imp_____ advice (not biased)

b) an inf_____ person (powerful)   i) mar_____ arts (judo, karate)

c) vir_____ reality (computerised)   j) a fac_____ account (based on facts)

d) a Greek st_____ (figure made of stone)

e) Con_____! (Well done!)   k) pun_____ (on time)

f) moi_____ (dampness)   l) a long lec_____ (talk)

g) int_____ debate (intelligent)   m) amb_____ (a goal, aim)

                                                    n) dep_____ time (leaving)

Read–cover–write

Read this sentence and remember it. Then cover it and write it underneath.

The competition was a partial success despite torrential rain.

_____

Check your spellings with the answers on page 43. Test yourself, or get a friend to test you.

I can spell all the words on this page. ☐   I can spell words with **ti** and **tu** endings. ☐

Topic words 2

Learn to spell these words. Take the word apart to look for the tricky bit. Then build it up to learn to spell it.

Read and look.	Write it. Take the word apart.	Write it. Find the tricky bit.	Remember it. Cover it. Write it.	Check. ✓
protein				
carbohydrate				
muscle				
oxygen				
circulation				
vessel				
evaporate				
temperature				
thermometer				

Read–cover–write

Read each sentence and remember it. Then cover the table and the sentence and write the sentence underneath.

Protein helps build muscle, while carbohydrate gives energy.

At what temperature did the liquid evaporate?

Blood vessels circulate oxygen round the body.

Prefixes in, im, ir and il

Remember

Double letters occur when these prefixes are added to words starting
m, r or l.   im-mortal   ir-resistible   il-legal   il-luminate

But not if the root word begins with a different letter.   inconvenience

Try it

1 Add the correct prefix (**in**, **im**, **ir** or **il**) to these root words. Write the
new word.

a) literate _____   g) logical _____   m) partial _____

b) capable _____   h) credible _____   n) definite _____

c) rational _____   i) relevant _____   o) moral _____

d) complete _____   j) mature _____   p) sincere _____

e) mobile _____   k) edible _____   q) precise _____

f) passable _____   l) movable _____   r) human _____

2 Replace the words shown in **bold** with negatives. Use the prefixes **in**, **im**,
ir and **il**.

a) The writing is **legible** _____ and **possible** _____ to read.

b) He is **patient** _____, **polite** _____ and **responsible** _____.

c) The chart is **accurate** _____ and the result **probable** _____

d) I know about **regular** _____ shapes and **proper** _____ fractions.

Read–cover–write

Read this sentence and remember it. Then cover it and write it underneath.

Once you become invisible the change will be irreversible.

_____

Check your spellings with the answers on page 43. Test yourself, or get a friend to test you.

I can spell all the words on this page. ☐   I can spell words with **in**, **im**, **ir** and **il** prefixes. ☐

More **ad** prefixes

Remember

These prefixes are all related to the prefix **ad**. Often, but not always, adding them results in double letters.

af-fix   ap-pear   at-tain   ac-cord   ar-rears

 But there is no double **d** in **ad**vantage because it is **ad**-vantage.

Try it

1 Write out each word so you can see the prefix and the root word.

a) accompany ____ _____   f) appeal ____ _____   k) acclaim ____ _____

b) attack ____ _____   g) address ____ _____   l) arrange ____ _____

c) attempt ____ _____   h) attend ____ _____   m) afloat ____ _____

d) approve ____ _____   i) assure ____ _____   n) apply ____ _____

e) approach ____ _____   j) arrest ____ _____   o) account ____ _____

2 Add the correct prefix from the pink box to complete these words.

ac   ad   af   at   ap   ar   as

a) ____mit   e) ____fect   i) ____pect   m) ____cept   q) ____flict

b) ____sess   f) ____vance   j) ____cuse   n) ____ore   r) ____tach

c) ____quit   g) ____prehend   k) ____sume   o) ____jacent   s) ____parent

d) ____firm   h) ____mire   l) ____tract   p) ____ford   t) ____vise

Read–cover–write

Read this sentence and remember it. Then cover it and write it underneath.

When I arrive I will approach carefully and appeal for calm.

_____

Check your spellings with the answers on page 44. Test yourself, or get a friend to test you.

I can spell all the words on this page. ☐   I can spell words with **ad** prefixes. ☐

Detecting prefixes and roots

Remember

Not all words with prefixes have a complete root word. Often prefixes are added to a shorter root.   **pro-gress   pre-fer**

Top tip Recognising prefixes and roots will help you spell words.

Try it

1   Add a prefix **per**, **pro** or **pre** to make words from the roots in the pink box. Write each word in the correct box below.

mit vide dict form sist pose fect ceed tend cess vent tect

per	pro	pre

2   Look for the prefixes at the start of these words. Write over each prefix.

surround   support   submerge   suspend   suffer

3   Now add the prefixes in question 2 to the roots to spell more words.

a) _____ vive   d) _____ tain   g) _____ pense   j) _____ side   m) _____ mit

b) _____ ply   e) _____ pose   h) _____ fice   k) _____ tract   n) _____ plus

c) _____ vey   f) _____ scribe i) _____ pect   l) _____ fix   o) _____ ject

Read–cover–write

Read this sentence and remember it. Then cover it and write it underneath.

To survive, we must produce a perfect supply with no surplus.

_____

Check your spellings with the answers on page 44. Test yourself, or get a friend to test you.

I can spell all the words on this page. ☐   I can detect prefixes to help me spell words. ☐

Homophones

Remember

Some words that sound the same have different meanings and spellings.
rain – subject: weather   **rein** – subject: horses   **reign** – subject: royalty

Try it

1 Write in the correct spelling of the homophone for the subject given in brackets.

a) sell – _____ (human body)

b) prophet – _____ (business)

c) earn – _____ (container)

d) led – _____ (metals)

e) key – _____ (seaside)

f) vane – _____ (human body)

g) need – _____ (making bread)

h) peer – _____ (seaside)

i) freeze – _____ (art)

j) pray – _____ (wild animals)

k) alter – _____ (church)

l) root – _____ (maps)

m) symbol – _____ (instrument)

n) isle – _____ (gap between seats)

2 Complete these phrases by writing in pairs of homophones.

a) TV s_____; breakfast _____

b) first dr_____; icy dr_____

c) w_____ paper bin; w_____ line

d) early m_____ sun; in m_____

e) tomato s_____; water s_____

f) fa_____ decided; a summer f_____

g) c_____ a cold; tennis c_____

h) Be my g_____. You g_____ it!

Read–cover–write

Read this sentence and remember it. Then cover it and write it underneath.

The symbols on the map showed the route to the quay.

_____

Check your spellings with the answers on page 44. Test yourself, or get a friend to test you.

I can spell all the words on this page. ☐   I can choose the correct spelling of homophones. ☐

Revision 2

1 Write the word. Use the clue to help you.

a) le _____ (traditional story)

b) g _____ ne (the real thing)

c) ex _____ te (go over the top in description)

d) co _____ (bravery)

e) de _____ l (fraction of a number)

f) fo _____ (from somewhere else)

g) r _____ m (beat of music)

h) re _____ (leave a job)

i) co _____ (vertical list of numbers)

j) sol _____ (serious, grave)

2 Complete the missing adjective.

a) a c _____ driver (wary, careful)

b) i _____ disease (catching)

c) n _____ meal (nourishing)

d) sc _____ food (delicious)

e) e _____ work (vital)

f) po _____ problem (possible)

g) con _____ file (secret, private)

h) to _____ rain (pouring, heavy)

i) pr _____ metal (very valuable)

j) su _____ mind (not trusting)

k) ar _____ grass (not real, manmade)

l) An _____ Egypt

m) knocked unc _____ (not awake)

n) a v _____ dog (savage)

3 Read this recount. Check the spelling of the words with prefixes. Underline each word that is wrong. Write the correct spelling above it.

The ship had been distroyed. Only five lifeboats remained

afloat, cast adrift on the raging sea with no pretection.

It was aparent to all the passengers that they might not servive.

The dangers were imense. They knew that help might not arive

before the circling sharks atacked. A flare eluminated the night

sky – a last atempt to atract the attention of a passing ship.

> Check your spellings with the answers on page 44.

Topic words 3

Learn to spell these words. Take the word apart to look for the tricky bit. Then build it up to learn to spell it.

Read and look.	Write it. Take the word apart.	Write it. Find the tricky bit.	Remember it. Cover it. Write it.	Check. ✓
digital				
calculator				
negative				
equilateral				
isosceles				
triangular				
radius				
diameter				
approximately				
kilogram				

Read–cover–write

Read each sentence and remember it. Then cover the table and the sentence and write the sentence underneath.

Equilateral and isosceles are types of triangular shape.

_____

Measure the radius and diameter of the cylinder/circle.

_____

The digital calculator showed a negative number.

_____

Adding suffixes: words ending e

Remember

Drop the e to add vowel suffixes; keep the e to add consonant suffixes.
hope → hoping hoped hopeful hopeless

There are a few exceptions.   canoe → canoeing   tie → tying

Try it

1   Use the rule to complete the grid.

root word	+ ing	+ ed	+ ful	+ less
care				
tune				
shame				
use				

2   Add the suffixes in **bold** to the root word. Write the new word.

a) achieve **ed** _____

b) disgrace **ful** _____

c) extreme **ist** _____

d) mistake **en** _____

e) measure **ing** _____

f) lie **ing** _____

g) reverse **al** _____

h) scarce **ly** _____

i) arrange **ment** _____

j) require **ment** _____

k) refuse **al** _____

l) complete **ness** _____

Read–cover–write

Read this sentence and remember it. Then cover it and write it underneath.

The arrival of the stranger came with no announcement.

_____

Check your spellings with the answers on page 45. Test yourself, or get a friend to test you.

I can spell all the words on this page. ☐   I can add suffixes to words ending with e. ☐

Adding suffixes: words ending y

Remember

Change y to i to add all suffixes except **ing**.
pity → pitiful pitied pitying

There are a few exceptions.   shy → shyness shyly

Try it

1 Use the rule to complete the word grid.

root word	+ er	+ est	+ ly	+ ness
heavy				
guilty				
ready				
healthy				

2 Add suffixes from the pink box to the root words. Write as many words as you can.

> ing ed er est al s ful ly ness able

tidy _____

fancy _____

deny _____

dry _____

Read–cover–write

Read this sentence and remember it. Then cover it and write it underneath.

There was no denying that she was easily the most beautiful of all.

_____

Check your spellings with the answers on page 45. Test yourself, or get a friend to test you.

I can spell all the words on this page. ☐   I can add suffixes to words ending with y. ☐

Adding suffixes: double the last letter

Remember

Double the last letter to add vowel suffixes such as **ed, er, est, en, ing** and **y.**   kidnap → kidnapper   picnic → picnicked

But not if the word ends with an unstressed syllable.   target → targeted

Try it

1 Add the **bold** vowel suffix and write the new word.

a) begin **er** _____

b) commit **ed** _____

c) equip **ed** _____

d) admit **ance** _____

e) panic **ing** _____

f) panic **y** _____

g) forgot **en** _____

h) travel **er** _____

i) omit **ed** _____

j) forbid **ing** _____

k) picnic **er** _____

l) picnic **ing** _____

m) permit **ed** _____

n) forbid **en** _____

o) regret **ing** _____

p) admit **ing** _____

q) panic **ed** _____

r) mimic **ing** _____

2 These words end with an unstressed syllable. Add **ing** to write the new word.

a) develop _____

b) limit _____

c) edit _____

d) fidget _____

e) gossip _____

f) orbit _____

g) market _____

h) plummet _____

i) gallop _____

j) profit _____

k) target _____

l) budget _____

Read–cover–write

Read this sentence and remember it. Then cover it and write it underneath.

The beginner pilot admitted to panicking as his plane plummeted.

_____

Check your spellings with the answers on page 45. Test yourself, or get a friend to test you.

I can spell all the words on this page. ☐   I can use the double consonant rule to add suffixes. ☐

Words ending **ous**

See also pages 28 and 29.

Remember

In many words, **ous** follows the normal rules for adding a vowel suffix.
nerve → nervous   industry → industrious

But sometimes unexpected changes are required.   vigour → vigorous

Try it

1 Use the normal rules to add **ous** to these words. Write the new words.

a) victory _____   d) marvel _____   g) mischief _____

b) rebel _____   e) fury _____   h) adventure _____

c) ridicule _____   f) vary _____   i) continue _____

2 Complete this table. Write in the root word and the change in spelling.

Root word	Adjective with **ous**	How the root changes
	wondrous	
	miraculous	
	humorous	
	outrageous	

3 The letter **e** is used to join **ous** to these words. Complete the words.

hid_____   court_____   pit_____   beaut_____   gas_____   gorg_____

Read–cover–write

Read this sentence and remember it. Then cover it and write it underneath.

The courageous villagers had a miraculous escape from the disastrous event.

_____

Check your spellings with the answers on page 45. Test yourself, or get a friend to test you.

I can spell all the words on this page. ☐   I can add **ous** to many words. ☐

Words ending **able** and **ible** (See also pages 28 and 29.)

Remember

In most words, adding **able** follows the normal rules for adding a vowel suffix.   dispose → disposable

But words ending soft **c** or soft **g** retain the **e** to keep the soft sound.
replace → replaceable

Try it

1 Add **able** to these words to make an adjective. Write the adjective.

a) argue _____

b) rely _____

c) notice _____

d) interchange _____

e) unstop _____

f) achieve _____

g) excite _____

h) vary _____

i) change _____

j) untrace _____

k) forget _____

l) pleasure _____

m) imagine _____

n) deny _____

o) unmanage _____

p) recharge _____

q) regret _____

r) honour _____

2 The missing words all end with **ible**. Use the clues to complete the words.

a) 10 is d_____ by 2 (can be divided)

b) fl_____ material (bendy)

c) ir_____ behaviour (reckless)

d) easily ac_____ (easy to get to)

e) fully c_____ (folds away)

f) a c_____ car (with fold-down roof)

g) ir_____ (cannot be resisted)

h) a pl_____ story (sounds likely)

Read–cover–write

Read this sentence and remember it. Then cover it and write it underneath.

Are rechargeable batteries more reliable than disposable ones?

_____

Check your spellings with the answers on page 46. Test yourself, or get a friend to test you.

I can spell all the words on this page. ☐   I can spell words ending in **able** and **ible**. ☐

Topic words 4

Learn to spell these words. Take the word apart to look for the tricky bit. Then build it up to learn to spell it.

Read and look.	Write it. Take the word apart.	Write it. Find the tricky bit.	Remember it. Cover it. Write it.	Check. ✓
simile				
metaphor				
alliteration				
onomatopoeia				
repetition				
imagery				
opinion				
rhetorical				
thesaurus				
vocabulary				

Read–cover–write

Read each sentence and remember it. Then cover the table and the sentence and write the sentence underneath.

In my opinion the metaphor is more effective than the simile.

_____

The poet used alliteration and onomatopoeia in the chorus.

_____

I use a thesaurus to improve my vocabulary.

_____

Word structure

Remember

Many words are created by adding affixes to root words, so thinking about how a word is formed will help you to spell it.

re place ment   sup press ion

Try it

1 Use the prefixes and suffixes in the pink box to make new words from the root word.

Prefixes: **dis   re   un   ap**   Suffixes: **ed   ful   able   ly   al   er**

colour _____

claim _____

prove _____

cover _____

ply _____

2 Write the parts of each word to show how it is formed.

a) prematurely _____   e) indigestion _____

b) recreation _____   f) injustice _____

c) prescription _____   g) misinformation _____

d) inconsiderate _____   h) unashamedly _____

Read—cover—write

Read this sentence and remember it. Then cover it and write it underneath.

Doctor, do I need a prescription for indigestion medication?

_____

Check your spellings with the answers on page 46. Test yourself, or get a friend to test you.

I can spell all the words on this page. ☐   I can build words using roots and affixes. ☐

Word families

Remember

Thinking about word families and words linked by meaning can give you a clue to spelling words.   **medic   medical   medicine**

Try it

1 Write the root or other family word that will help you spell these words.

a) pleasure _____

b) equator _____

c) familiar _____

d) superior _____

e) majority _____

f) history _____

g) southern _____

h) citizen _____

i) pressure _____

j) wisdom _____

k) percentage _____

l) publicity _____

m) marriage _____

n) lawyer _____

o) circuit _____

2 Complete this table. Write in the root word and extra words with the same root.

root word	family word 1	family word 2	family word 3
	signal	signature	
	actor	activity	
	variety		
	describe		

Read–cover–write

Read this sentence and remember it. Then cover it and write it underneath.

The actor signed his signature with definite pleasure.

_____

Check your spellings with the answers on page 46. Test yourself, or get a friend to test you.

I can spell all the words on this page. ☐   I can spell words with the same root or meaning. ☐

35

Word histories

Remember

Knowing the history and meaning of word roots can help you to spell words.   prim (meaning first): **prime   primary   primitive   primrose**

Try it

1 Write over the Greek and Latin roots at the start of these words.

automobile   aeroplane   aquamarine   audible

2 Use the roots from question 1 to complete the words.

a) _____ matic   d) _____ lung   g) _____ tion   j) _____ tic

b) _____ rium   e) _____ graph   h) _____ pilot   k) _____ cue

c) _____ drome   f) _____ bics   i) _____ sol   l) _____ ence

3 Add the root shown in **bold** to spell the five related words.

circu: _____ mference, _____ late, _____ s, _____ lar, _____ lation

graph: tele _____ , photo _____ , _____ ic, para _____ , _____ ite

inter: _____ val, _____ rupt, _____ view, _____ fere, _____ lude

cent: per _____ age, _____ ury, _____ igrade, _____ imetre, _____ ipede

4 Write each of the roots in questions 1 and 3 beside its meaning.

_____ = air   _____ = between   _____ = round   _____ = hear

_____ = self   _____ = write   _____ = hundred   _____ = water

Read–cover–write

Read this sentence and remember it. Then cover it and write it underneath.

The aeroplane was on autopilot as the captain addressed the audience.

_____

Check your spellings with the answers on page 46. Test yourself, or get a friend to test you.

I can spell all the words on this page. ☐   I can spell words with Greek and Latin roots. ☐

Common confusions

Remember

Some words are confused because they have similar spellings.

My team was **eliminated**.   The night sky was **illuminated**.

Top tip Use the sound and your knowledge to decide which word is correct.

Try it

1 Write the words from the box in the correct place to complete the sentence.

a) The skier made a d_____ d_____.

b) It is best to be w_____ when feeling w_____.

c) Which is the largest c_____ in the c_____?

d) Don't l_____ your l_____ tooth.

e) Zoe _____ red but I _____ blue.

> decent descent
>
> wary weary
>
> country county
>
> loose lose
>
> choose chose

2 Write the words from the box in the correct place.

a chocolate d_____   a sandy d_____

thunder and l_____   l_____ the mood

He is _____ to play.   The writing was _____.

He's a little _____.   This is a right _____.

April _____ May.   She p_____ to the start.

Write in your _____.   milk from the d_____

> dessert desert
>
> lightening lightning
>
> eligible illegible
>
> angel angle
>
> proceeds precedes
>
> dairy diary

Read–cover–write

Read this sentence and remember it. Then cover it and write it underneath.

Choose a decent pair of boots and proceed to the dairy.

_____

Check your spellings with the answers on page 47. Test yourself, or get a friend to test you.

I can spell all the words on this page. ☐   I can choose the correct word. ☐

Revision 3

1 **Read the clue and write the word.**

a) a_____ic (runs by itself)

b) a_____um (tank for fish)

c) a_____ol (spray can)

d) a_____ce (viewers/listeners)

e) i_____w (question someone)

f) c_____ (100 years)

g) t_____pe (use it to see the stars)

h) e_____r (round the Earth's middle)

i) va_____y (assortment)

j) d_____te (certain, exact)

k) m_____re (small version)

l) c_____ce (distance round a circle)

2 **Write the synonym for the word shown in bold.**

a) a **beautiful** g_____s day

b) an **ugly** h_____s monster

c) a **funny** h_____s story

d) in **different** v_____ sizes

e) a **brave** c_____ hero

f) an **amazing** m_____ escape

g) a **wonderful** mar_____ holiday

h) a **silly** r_____ idea

i) It is just **readable** l_____.

j) The target was **possible** ach_____.

3 **Read this extract from a story. Check the spelling of words with suffixes. Underline each word that is wrong. Write the correct spelling above it.**

Carfully, Simeon tyied the laces on his trainers. He felt extremly nerveous

waiting for the race to start. Then the gun fired and they were off!

To his amazment Simeon found he was in the leading group. But the

race was just begining. It would test his fittness, determination and

readyness for the challenge. Soon he felt the chaseing pack was getting

closer. But Simeon was determinned not to be beatten. He felt unstopable.

Check your spellings with the answers on page 47.

Personal spelling list

Look through examples of your writing for words that you keep spelling wrongly. Use a dictionary to find the correct spellings and copy the words into the first column. Then learn to spell them.

Read and look.	Write it. Take the word apart.	Write it. Find the tricky bit.	Remember it. Cover it. Write it.	Check. ✓

Read–cover–write

Make up your own spelling sentences to help you practise them.

_____

_____

_____

Answers

Page 4

1
a) de fi **n**ite
b) mess **en** ger
c) en v**e** lope
d) ge n**er** al
e) se p**a** rate
f) con si d**er** ing
g) a v**er** age
h) des p**er** ate
i) rel **e** vant
j) se v**er** al
k) pri vi l**eg**e
l) li t**er** ate

2
a) similar
b) regular
c) reason
d) dandelion
e) miracle
f) instrument
g) secretary
h) vegetable
i) purpose
j) challenge
k) benefit
l) company
m) popular
n) wizard
o) villain
p) horizon
q) garage
r) manage
s) hurricane
t) develop

Page 5

1
a) off**er** ing
b) free d**om**
c) origin **al**
d) marv**e**l lous
e) pr**e** pare
f) consid**er** able
g) mis**er** able
h) form **al**
i) prosp**er** ous
j) pois**on** ous
k) natur[e] al
l) t**o** morrow

2
a) deafening
b) widening
c) jewellery (*or* jewelry)
d) sharpener
e) frightening
f) straighteners
g) imaginary
h) whitener/whitening

Page 6

1
a) A robber, an archer and a potter visited the prisoner.
b) The sailor, the doctor and the inventor met the inspector.
c) A beggar and a burglar met the vicar in the cellar.
d) An author, an editor, an actor and a director met an art collector.
e) The grocer, the baker, the builder and the butcher need a customer.

2
a) sensor
b) collar
c) mirror
d) metre
e) visitor
f) operator
g) grammar
h) monitor
i) fibre
j) radiator
k) horror
l) professor
m) calendar
n) litre
o) reflector
p) elevator
q) error
r) solar
s) theatre
t) alligator
u) caterpillar
v) terror
w) sponsor
x) centre
y) tractor

Page 7

1
a) mystery
b) factory
c) memory
d) nursery
e) burglary
f) dictionary
g) delivery
h) diary
i) forgery
j) archery
k) February
l) recovery
m) discovery
n) victory
o) glossary
p) battery
q) primary
r) secondary
s) ordinary
t) misery

2
a) boundary
b) voluntary
c) directory
d) lottery
e) surgery
f) summary
g) category
h) military
i) gallery
j) machinery

Page 8

1
a) direction
b) magician
c) intrusion
d) procession
e) permission
f) optician
g) reduction
h) electrician
i) completion
j) transfusion
k) impression
l) inclusion

2
a) operate, operation
b) celebrate, celebration
c) communicate, communication
d) terminate, termination
e) demonstrate, demonstration
f) imitate, imitation
g) exaggerate, exaggeration
h) ventilate, ventilation
i) illustrate, illustration
j) equate, equation

Page 10

1

au makes an 'or' sound	au makes a different sound
daughter, taunt, haul, trauma, pause, naughty, dinosaur	aunt, sausage, beauty, draught, laughter

2
a) saucepan
b) restaurant
c) exhausted
d) haughty
e) applause
f) laundry
g) beautiful
h) haunted
i) slaughter
j) clause

Page 11

1
a) ourselves – scour
b) courage – nourish
c) tour – detour
d) court – course
e) hour – devour
f) glamour – honour
g) favour – vigour
h) mourn – source
i) savour – behaviour
j) savoury – favourite

2
a) downpour
b) odour
c) vapour
d) harbour
e) mournful
f) armour
g) labour
h) neighbour
i) rumour
j) tourist
k) humour
l) journalist

Page 12

1
a) cough
b) tough
c) brought
d) trough
e) rough
f) bough
g) borough
h) dough
i) though
j) fought
k) plough
l) thorough

2
rough and tough
plough and bough
trough and cough
fought and brought
though and dough
thorough and borough

3
a) enough
b) sought
c) ought
d) thoughtless
e) drought
f) although/though
g) bought
h) thoroughly (*or* throughout)

Page 13

1
a) grief
b) relief
c) receipt
d) mischief
e) fiend
f) deceive
g) wield
h) receive
i) shriek
j) niece
k) achieve
l) grieve
m) ceiling
n) conceit
o) perceive

2

ie not long 'e' sound	ei long 'a' sound	ei other sound
quiet, fiery, view	sleigh, veil, reign, vein	height, weird, neither, either, seize

Page 14

1 The knight came to a <u>buetiful</u> [beautiful] field of <u>colorful</u> [colourful] flowers. The sight cheered him and he <u>laghed</u> [laughed] as he thought of the five <u>peices</u> [pieces] of silver he <u>beleived</u> [believed] he would <u>recieve</u> [receive] for rescuing the king's <u>favorite</u> [favourite] <u>dauhgter</u> [daughter]. But suddenly, a <u>mornful</u> [mournful] sound <u>peirced</u> [pierced] the silence. His horse was <u>thorughly</u> [thoroughly] spooked and the knight's <u>curage</u> [courage] once more deserted him.

2
a) Families
b) factories
c) galleries
d) batteries
e) surgeries
f) memories
g) estimate
h) operate
i) narrate
j) demonstrate
k) create
l) punctuate

3 <u>Yesturday</u> [Yesterday] I went cycling with my <u>famaly</u> [family]. Mum said it would be <u>intresting</u> [interesting] to try something <u>diffrent</u> [different] for a change. We must have cycled for <u>sevral</u> [several] hours. None of us fell off, which was quite good <u>considring</u> [considering] how <u>differcult</u> [difficult] the path was. But then the sky <u>darkend</u> [darkened] and it was no <u>suprise</u> [surprise] when it began to rain. <u>Natrally</u> [Naturally] we had a <u>misrable</u> [miserable] ride back. Still, I would <u>defenately</u> [definitely] go again.

Page 16

1
a) decimal
b) vacancy
c) recite
d) cemetery
e) sincere
f) cyclone
g) decent
h) council
i) success
j) exceed
k) incident
l) innocent
m) process
n) scenic
o) fancy
p) fascinate
q) cigar
r) mercy ('merci' is a French word)
s) convince
t) capacity

2
a) central
b) citizen
c) century
d) cyclist
e) recent
f) decision
g) cylinder
h) cinema
i) magnificent
j) concern
k) succeed
l) certificate

Page 17

1
a) musician
b) spacious
c) optician
d) suspicious
e) politician
f) delicious
g) vicious
h) ancient
i) gracious
j) luscious
k) financial
l) precious
m) conscious
n) efficient
o) special
p) social
q) sufficient
r) artificial
s) racial
t) malicious

2
a) accelerate
b) accident
c) document
d) spectacular
e) evacuate
f) curious
g) accent
h) eccentric
i) calculate
j) occupy
k) accurate
l) peculiar

Page 18

1.
a) gigantic/giant
b) genius
c) genuine
d) gently
e) gymnast
f) generous
g) genie
h) germs
i) gesture (*or* gesticulate)
j) gyrate

2.
a) rigid
b) emergency
c) dungeon
d) gadget
e) agile
f) apology
g) origin
h) legend
i) engineer
j) digit
k) judgement
l) privilege
m) tragic
n) suggestion
o) agent
p) exaggerate
q) logic
r) gorgeous

Page 19

1.
a) limb
b) honest
c) tomb
d) plumber
e) honeycomb
f) knead
g) scent
h) scheme
i) receipt
j) hustle

2.
a) doubt
b) rhythm
c) wretched
d) campaign
e) design
f) wreath
g) reign
h) rhombus
i) wring
j) foreign
k) condemn
l) rhino
m) column
n) subtle
o) resign
p) rhubarb
q) debt
r) wrench
s) hymn
t) solemn

Page 20

1.
a) partial
b) confidential
c) infectious
d) potential
e) scrumptious
f) torrential
g) ambitious
h) patient
i) nutritious
j) cautious
k) residential
l) essential

2.
a) substantial
b) influential
c) virtual
d) statue
e) Congratulations!
f) moisture
g) intellectual
h) impartial
i) martial
j) factual
k) punctual
l) lecture
m) ambition/ambitious
n) departure

Page 22

1.
a) illiterate
b) incapable
c) irrational
d) incomplete
e) immobile
f) impassable
g) illogical
h) incredible
i) irrelevant
j) immature
k) inedible
l) immovable
m) impartial
n) indefinite
o) immoral
p) insincere
q) imprecise
r) inhuman

2.
a) The writing is <u>illegible</u> and <u>impossible</u> to read.
b) He is <u>impatient</u>, <u>impolite</u> and <u>irresponsible</u>.
c) The chart is <u>inaccurate</u> and the result <u>improbable</u>.
d) I know about <u>irregular</u> shapes and <u>improper</u> fractions.

Page 23

1
a) ac company
b) at tack
c) at tempt
d) ap prove
e) ap proach
f) ap peal
g) ad dress
h) at tend
i) as sure
j) ar rest
k) ac claim
l) ar range
m) a float
n) ap ply
o) ac count

2
a) admit
b) assess
c) acquit
d) affirm
e) affect
f) advance
g) apprehend
h) admire
i) aspect
j) accuse
k) assume
l) attract
m) accept
n) adore/afore
o) adjacent
p) afford
q) afflict
r) attach
s) apparent
t) advise

Page 24

1

per	pro	pre
permit, perform, persist, perfect	provide, propose, proceed, process, protect	predict, prefect, pretend, prevent

3
a) survive
b) supply
c) survey
d) sustain
e) suppose
f) subscribe
g) suspense
h) suffice
i) suspect
j) subside
k) subtract
l) suffix
m) submit
n) surplus
o) subject

Page 25

1
a) sell – cell
b) prophet – profit
c) earn – urn
d) led – lead
e) key – quay
f) vane – vein
g) need – knead
h) peer – pier
i) freeze – frieze
j) pray – prey
k) alter – altar
l) root – route
m) symbol – cymbal
n) isle – aisle

2
a) serial – cereal
b) draft – draught
c) waste – waist
d) morning – mourning
e) sauce – source
f) fate – fete
g) caught – court
h) guest – guessed

Page 26

1
a) legend
b) genuine
c) exaggerate
d) courage
e) decimal
f) foreign
g) rhythm
h) resign
i) column
j) solemn

2
a) cautious
b) infectious
c) nutritious
d) scrumptious
e) essential
f) potential
g) confidential
h) torrential
i) precious
j) suspicious
k) artificial
l) Ancient
m) unconscious
n) vicious

3
The ship had been distroyed [destroyed]. Only five lifeboats remained affloat [afloat], cast adrift on the raging sea with no pretection [protection]. It was aparent [apparent] to all the passengers that they might not servive [survive]. The dangers were imense [immense]. They knew that help might not arive [arrive] before the circling sharks atacked [attacked]. A flare eluminated [illuminated] the night sky – a last atempt [attempt] to atract [attract] the attention of a passing ship.

Page 28

1

root word	+ ing	+ ed	+ ful	+ less
care	caring	cared	careful	careless
tune	tuning	tuned	tuneful	tuneless
shame	shaming	shamed	shameful	shameless
use	using	used	useful	useless

2
a) achieved
b) disgraceful
c) extremist
d) mistaken
e) measuring
f) lying
g) reversal
h) scarcely
i) arrangement
j) requirement
k) refusal
l) completeness

Page 29

1

root word	+ er	+ est	+ ly	+ ness
heavy	heavier	heaviest	heavily	heaviness
guilty	guiltier	guiltiest	guiltily	guiltiness
ready	readier	readiest	readily	readiness
healthy	healthier	healthiest	healthily	healthiness

2
Possible answers include:
tidy – tidying, tidied, tidier, tidiest, tidies, tidily, tidiness
fancy – fancying, fancied, fancier, fanciest, fancies, fanciful, fancifully, fancily, fanciness
deny – denying, denied, denier, denial, denies, deniable
dry – drying, dried, drier, dryer, driest, dries, drily, dryness, dryable

Page 30

1
a) beginner
b) committed
c) equipped
d) admittance
e) panicking
f) panicky
g) forgotten
h) traveller
i) omitted
j) forbidding
k) picnicker
l) picnicking
m) permitted
n) forbidden
o) regretting
p) admitting
q) panicked
r) mimicking

2
a) developing
b) limiting
c) editing
d) fidgeting
e) gossiping
f) orbiting
g) marketing
h) plummeting
i) galloping
j) profiting
k) targeting
l) budgeting

Page 31

1
a) victorious
b) rebellious
c) ridiculous
d) marvellous
e) furious
f) various
g) mischievous
h) adventurous
i) continuous

2

Root word	How the root changes
wonder	drop the **e** from **er** ending
miracle	**le** changes to **ul**
humour	drop the **u** from **our** ending
outrage	keep the final **e** on **ge**

3
hideous, courteous, piteous, beauteous, gaseous, gorgeous

Page 32

1
a) arguable
b) reliable
c) noticeable
d) interchangeable
e) unstoppable
f) achievable
g) excitable
h) variable
i) changeable
j) untraceable
k) forgettable
l) pleasurable
m) imaginable
n) deniable
o) unmanageable
p) rechargeable
q) regrettable
r) honourable

2
a) divisible
b) flexible
c) irresponsible
d) accessible
e) collapsible
f) convertible
g) irresistible
h) plausible

Page 34

1 *Possible answers include:*
colour: discolour, discoloured, uncoloured, coloured, colourful, colourfully
claim: disclaimed, disclaimer, reclaimed, unclaimed, reclaimable, claimable
prove: disprove, disproved, reprove, unproved, approved, approval, disapproval, provable
cover: discover, discovered, recover, recovered, recoverable, unrecoverable, covered
ply: replied, replier, applied, applier, reapplied

2
a) pre mature ly
b) re creat[e] ion
c) pre script ion
d) in consider ate
e) in digest ion
f) in just ice
g) mis in form ation
h) un a sham[e] ed ly

Page 35

1
a) please
b) equate/equal
c) family
d) super
e) major
f) story
g) south
h) city
i) press
j) wise
k) cent
l) public
m) marry
n) law
o) circle

2 *Possible answers include:*
sign: design, resign, resignation
act: action, reaction, counteract
vary: various, variable, variation
scribe: scribble, transcribe, description

Page 36

2
a) automatic
b) aquarium
c) aerodrome
d) aqualung
e) autograph
f) aerobics
g) audition
h) autopilot
i) aerosol
j) aquatic
k) autocue
l) audience

3
circu: circumference, circulate, circus, circular, circulation
graph: telegraph, photograph, graphic, paragraph, graphite
inter: interval, interrupt, interview, interfere, interlude
cent: percentage, century, centigrade, centimetre, centipede

4
aero = air
auto = self
inter = between
graph = write
circu = round
cent = hundred
audi = hear
aqua = water

Page 37

1

a) The skier made a decent descent.
b) It is best to be wary when feeling weary.
c) Which is the largest county in the country?
d) Don't lose your loose tooth.
e) Zoe chose red but I choose blue.

2

a chocolate dessert	a sandy desert
thunder and lightning	lightening the mood
He is eligible to play.	The writing was illegible.
He's a little angel.	This is a right angle.
April precedes May.	She proceeds to the start.
Write in your diary.	milk from the dairy

Page 38

1

a) automatic
b) aquarium
c) aerosol
d) audience
e) interview
f) century
g) telescope
h) equator
i) variety
j) definite
k) miniature
l) circumference

2

a) glorious
b) hideous
c) humorous
d) various
e) courageous
f) miraculous
g) marvellous
h) ridiculous
i) legible
j) achievable

3 Carfully [Carefully], Simeon tyied [tied] the laces on his trainers. He felt extremly [extremely] nerveous [nervous] waiting for the race to start. Then the gun fired and they were off! To his amazment [amazement] Simeon found he was in the leading group. But the race was just begining [beginning]. It would test his fittness [fitness], determination and readyness [readiness] for the challenge. Soon he felt the chaseing [chasing] pack was getting closer. But Simeon was determinned [determined] not to be beatten [beaten]. He felt unstopable [unstoppable].

Published by Schofield & Sims Ltd,
Dogley Mill, Fenay Bridge, Huddersfield HD8 0NQ, UK
Tel 01484 607080

First published in 2013
© Schofield & Sims Ltd, 2013

Author: Carol Matchett
Carol Matchett has asserted her moral right under the Copyright, Designs and Patents Act, 1988, to be identified as the author of this work.

British Library Cataloguing in Publication Data
A catalogue record for this book is available from the British Library.
Commissioned by Carolyn Richardson Publishing Services
(www.publiserve.co.uk)

Design by Oxford Designers & Illustrators
Printed in the UK by Page Bros (Norwich) Limited

ISBN 978 07217 1216 1

Schofield&Sims

Learn to spell in three simple steps
Remember • Try it • Read–cover–write

Accurate spelling improves fluency in writing and is vital to clear communication. **Schofield & Sims Spelling** is a structured and rigorous programme designed for Key Stages 1 and 2 – but also suitable for some older students. At the heart of the programme is a set of six pupil books, accessible to all who have a basic understanding of letter–sound relationships. Correct answers are provided at the back of each book so that pupils may mark their own work.

Ideal for both whole-school and independent learning, this comprehensive and high-quality series builds on pupils' phonic knowledge while also helping them to understand how word structure and meaning can help them to spell words. Providing excellent preparation for the **English grammar, punctuation and spelling tests** at the end of Key Stage 2, the **Schofield & Sims Spelling** activities:

*   systematically introduce spelling conventions – and revise those already taught

*   explore word structure and the relationship between words of shared origin

*   suggest strategies for remembering common 'exception words' (also known as 'tricky words')

*   teach pupils how to monitor and correct their own spelling

*   encourage them to write sentences from memory or dictation.

As pupils work through each book, the intensive practice provided will enable them continually to develop, consolidate and improve their skills, encouraging them towards effective spelling for life.

Areas covered by **Spelling 5** include:

*   using further prefixes and suffixes and applying rules for adding suffixes

*   spelling words with silent letters

*   using knowledge of word structure and word origins

*   learning to spell difficult words (for example, words with unstressed vowels, words with the letter string **ough**)

*   learning guidelines for word endings (for example **ary**, **ory**, **ery**, **tion**, **cian**, **cious**, **cial**, **tious**, **tial**, **able**, **ible**)

*   distinguishing between homophones and other words that are commonly confused.

Also available: a **Teacher's Guide**, providing detailed teaching notes that suggest how best to explain and explore each learning point, a **Teacher's Resource Book**, containing copymasters that support teaching, assessment and record-keeping, and **free downloads for teachers**, available from the Schofield & Sims website.

The complete range of books is as follows:

Spelling 1 (Key Stage 1)	ISBN 978 07217 1212 3	
Spelling 2 (Key Stage 1)	ISBN 978 07217 1213 0	
Spelling 3 (Key Stage 2)	ISBN 978 07217 1214 7	
Spelling Teacher's Guide	ISBN 978 07217 1218 5	
Spelling 4 (Key Stage 2)	ISBN 978 07217 1215 4
Spelling 5 (Key Stage 2)	ISBN 978 07217 1216 1
Spelling 6 (Key Stage 2)	ISBN 978 07217 1217 8
Spelling Teacher's Resource Book	ISBN 978 07217 1219 2

ISBN 978-07217-1216-1

9 780721 712161

FSC MIX Paper from responsible sources FSC® C023114

ISBN 978 07217 1216 1
Key Stages 1 & 2
Age range 5–12 years
£2.95
(Retail price)

For further information and to place your order visit
www.schofieldandsims.co.uk or telephone 01484 607080